4 Lisa goes upstairs to her room.

5 That evening, Lisa talks to a student in the hostel.

9 Michael has a camera. He looks at Lisa.

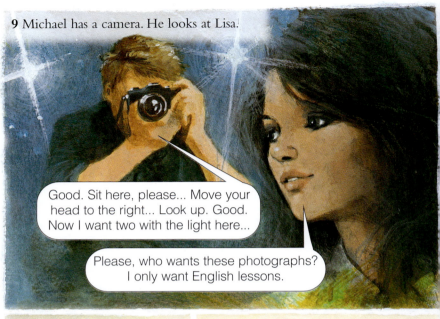

10 Michael doesn't understand.

11 Now Michael understands. Lisa wants the Alpha School, not the Alpha Studio!

21 In the morning, a car is waiting in the street for Lisa.

22 The driver stops the car and opens the door for Lisa.

23 Lisa goes in. Michael is waiting for her.

24 They go into a very big room. But what's this? Lions!

This is very exciting. But it's safe, Lisa. Look. This is glass. We're safe behind this glass.

Here's your costume, Lisa.

25 Michael takes the photos.

Wonderful, Lisa! Wonderful!

I'm crazy. This costume is crazy.

26 Michael finishes the photos. Lisa wants to go.

Can I go back to the school now? Are the photos OK?

Yes, they're going to be wonderful...

30 In the morning, Michael goes to the school.

31 The day after that...

32 Then Michael has the answer.

Lisa listens. Then she says, 'Yes.' Michael is happy. Lisa is happy, too. She can have her English lessons.

The ten days are wonderful. But then Michael and Lisa finish the hairspray job. Lisa goes back to school. She wants her real English lessons.

39 In the morning, Lisa is waiting for a taxi.

40 Lisa sees her photo in an advertisement. **41** At the airport...

ACTIVITIES

Pages 1–7

Before you read

1 Read the Word List at the back of the book.

    a Which of the twenty words can you put in these sentences?

        It is a ..... place.   It is an ..... place.

    b What are the twenty words in your language?

2 In this story, a girl goes to London for the first time. Why do people visit London? Talk about it.

While you read

3 Finish these sentences. Write one word.

    a Lisa stays in a .... in Moon Street.

    b She wants to learn .... English.

    c A student talks to her about Alpha ....

    d In Delmore Street, Michael takes .... of Lisa.

    e But Lisa is a student, not a ....

    f Michael works in the Alpha ....

    g Mr Craig wants Lisa for his Softspray ....

    h But Lisa doesn't want the ....

    i Michael's .... , Susan, talks to Lisa.

    j The job is very .... for Michael.

After you read

4 Work with a friend.

    Student A: You are Lisa. Telephone a British friend. Talk about your day at the studio.

    Student B: You are Lisa's friend. You live in Manchester. Ask about Lisa's first two days in London.

16

Pages 8–15

Before you read

5 Lisa is going to work with Michael. Talk about these questions. What do you think?

   a Is she going to like being a model?

   b Is Mr Craig going to be happy with the photos?

   c Is Lisa going to work for Michael again?

   d Is she going to learn any English?

While you read

6 Who is talking? Who or what are they talking about?

   a 'Is this the right place?' ....

   ....

   b 'They're going to be wonderful.' ....

   ....

   c 'She's important to you.' ....

   ....

   d 'What – *now*?' ....

   ....

   e 'I want photos from there.' ....

   ....

   f 'I know your face.' ....

   ....

After you read

7 Lisa wanted to learn English at a school, but can she learn English at work too? What do you think?

8 Lisa is famous and her photo is in a newspaper. Write about her for the same newspaper.

9 Do models have a good job? Why (not)? Write about it.

Answers for the Activities in this book are available from the Pearson English Readers website.
A free Activity Worksheet is also available from the website. Activity worksheets are
part of the Pearson English Readers Teacher Support Programme, which also includes
Progress tests and Graded Reader Guidelines. For more information, please visit:
www.pearsonenglishreaders.com.

WORD LIST *with example sentences*

advertisement (n) The job *advertisements* are at the back of the newspaper.

camera (n) I want to take a picture of that building. Have you got a *camera*?

costume (n) That's my brother, in the Father Christmas *costume*.

crazy (adj) You can't drive across Siberia in winter. That's *crazy*!

exciting (adj) It was *exciting* because it was my first visit to Japan.

glass (n) There is no *glass* in that window.

hairspray (n) Look at my hair! Have you got any *hairspray*.

hostel (n) She is staying in a small *hostel*, not a hotel.

last (adj) He stopped working because he was sixty-five *last* year.

lesson (n) They have English *lessons* after school.

lion (n) We went to Africa because we wanted to see *lions*.

model (n/v) Kate Moss isn't very tall, but she is a *model*.

ready (adj) Are you *ready*? We are going to be late.

real (adj) This isn't *real* money. It's from a children's game.

safe (adj) This street isn't *safe* for children. Cars drive down it very quickly.

secretary (n) Can't you find him? Ask his *secretary*.

studio (n) The photographer works in a *studio* in her home.

upstairs (adv) She is going *upstairs* to bed.

waste (n) The new coat was a *waste* of money. She doesn't like it now.

wonderful (adj) We had a *wonderful* holiday in Italy. We loved it.

Pearson Education Limited
Edinburgh Gate, Harlow,
Essex CM20 2JE, England
and Associated Companies throughout the world.

ISBN: 978-1-4058-7696-4

First published by Penguin Books 2000
This edition first published by Pearson Education 2008

13

Copyright © Pearson Education Ltd 2008
Illustrations by Brian Dennington

Typeset by Graphicraft Ltd, Hong Kong
Set in 12/14pt Bembo
Printed in China
SWTC/13

*All rights reserved; no part of this publication may be reproduced, stored
in a retrieval system, or transmitted in any form or by any means,
electronic, mechanical, photocopying, recording or otherwise, without the
prior written permission of the Publishers.*

Published by Pearson Education Ltd

Every effort has been made to trace the copyright holders and we apologise in advance for
any unintentional omissions. We would be pleased to insert the appropriate
acknowledgement in any subsequent edition of this publication.

For a complete list of the titles available in the Pearson English Readers series, please
visit www.pearsonenglishreaders.com. Alternatively, write to your local Pearson Education
office or to Pearson English Readers Marketing Department, Pearson Education,
Edinburgh Gate, Harlow, Essex CM20 2JE, England.